Can You the Wagon?

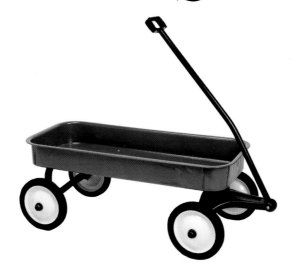

Katacha Díaz

Can you see the dog?

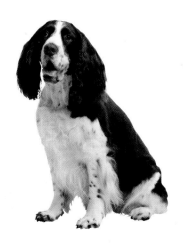
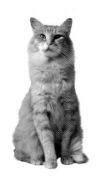
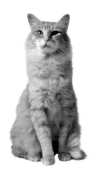
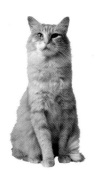

3

Can you see the block?

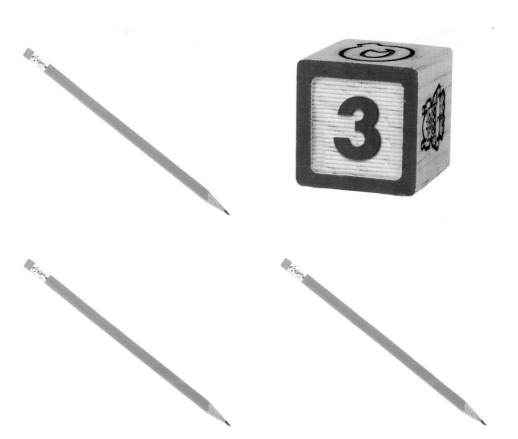

Can you see the doll?

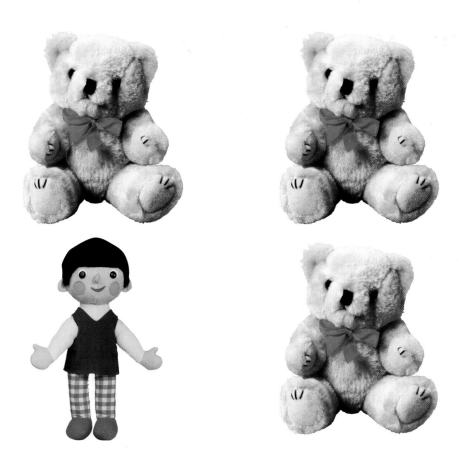

Can you see the car?

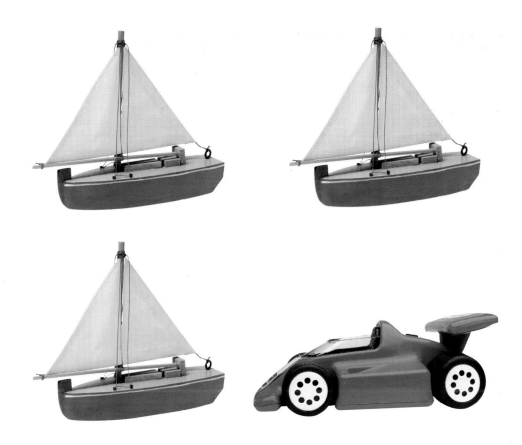

Can you see the book?

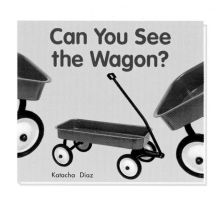

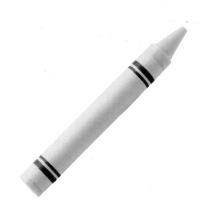

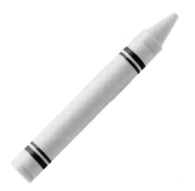

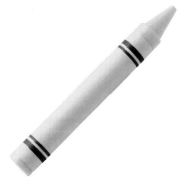

Can you see the truck?

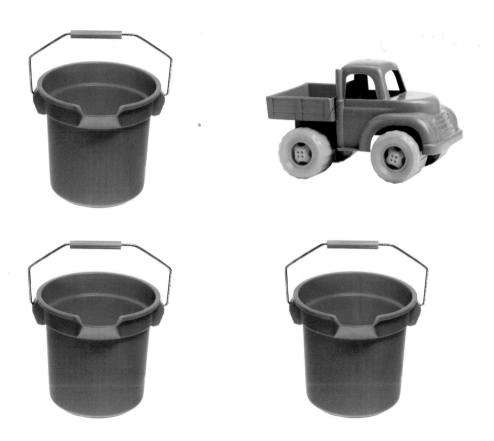

Can you see the ball?

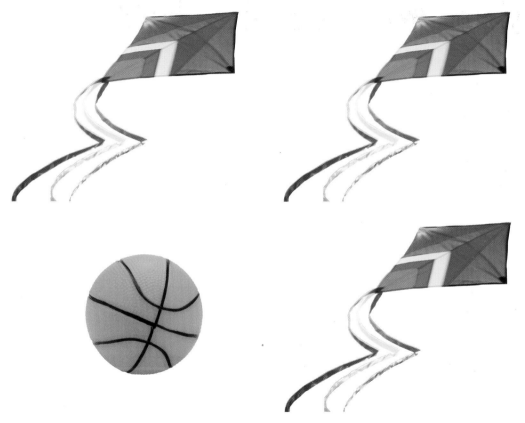

Can you see the wagon?

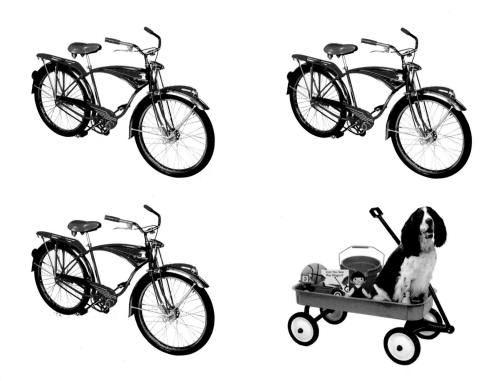